In
More Years

by Julie Verne
illustrated by Anne Kennedy

Orlando   Boston   Dallas   Chicago   San Diego

Visit *The Learning Site!*

www.harcourtschool.com

In eight more years, I'll be a clerk
at the ice-cream store. My sister,
Beth, was an ice-cream store clerk. It
was her first real job.

One time she was "Clerk of the Week." A poster was put up to honor her for being good at her job. Beth was very proud of it.

Now that Beth is grown up, she has a different job. Now she is a mail carrier, and she likes this job better.

Beth's job is a lot of work. There
are 369 homes on her route. First
she has to sort the mail for all of
these homes. She has to be careful
so she doesn't mix up people's mail.

Then she puts the mail in big trays. You can imagine how heavy each tray is when it's full. Beth says it's as much as 35 pounds!

Beth carries the trays one by one to the truck. Before she loads them, she has to put all of the boxes onto the truck. Then she stacks the trays in the truck.

Beth says that mail carriers need strong legs. Some of them have to walk a lot on their routes. Beth does. She walks about seven miles a day.

Dogs can be a danger to Beth when she is on her route. Some dogs like Beth and don't bother her. Others bark or growl. Beth says, "I'm always on the lookout for dogs."

During the holidays there is even more mail to deliver. At these times, Beth has extra work to do.

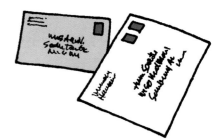

A mail carrier's job is easier to do in some kinds of weather than in others. When rain pours down, Beth puts on her rain clothes. Mail carriers must deliver the mail in all kinds of weather every day.

When Beth has finished delivering the mail, she drives to several mailboxes. The mail will pour out into the empty trays.

I wonder where all of that mail is going. The mail from just one mailbox may be sent to addresses in hundreds of cities and towns. Isn't that amazing?

Beth's truck is very interesting. Did you ever notice that the steering wheel in a mail truck is on the right-hand side?

That way the mail carrier doesn't have to get out to put mail in a roadside mailbox.

In eight more years, I might be a clerk at an ice-cream store. Later on I think I'll be a mail carrier too—just like Beth.